A Galway Tale

Claddagh
The Tale of the Ring

By
Patricia McAdoo

Illustrated by
James Newell

GALWAY ONLINE | GALWAYONLINE.COM

Special Thanks
Our thanks to Jim Higgins, Heritage Officer, Galway City Council for his help.
To Stan O'Reilly at Claddagh Jewellers for explaining the craft of the jeweller
and to Imelda Heaphy for her proof-reading assistance.

ISBN 0-9551652-0-2

Written by Patricia McAdoo.
Based on a story outline by Robert Smyth.
Copyright © 2005 Patricia McAdoo and Robert Smyth.

Illustrations Copyright © 2005 Galway Online.

Published by Galway Online, Knocknacarra, Galway.
tales@galwayonline.com
www.galwayonline.com

First published October 2005.

Produced and printed in Galway, Ireland.

I grew up in the Claddagh, a fishing village across the bridge from the walls of Galway town. My father was a fisherman and right below our cottage was a slipway where, on clear mornings, the boats set sail, to return heaving and jumping with slippery mackerel and cod. The smell of fish always lingered on the air.

Grandfather lived with us and he was so tall that he had to bend very low to come through the doorway. He spent his days sitting outside, watching the world go by and carving pieces of old bogwood. Every year, before the winter set in, he borrowed an ass and cart and went west to the bogs above Barna. When he came back, the cart was loaded with stretches of wood, which he carved into figures during the long evenings.

Everyone in the Claddagh knew my grandfather. When I was eleven years old, he carved a boat for me, a white sailed cutter, with cloth sails of calico. Me and my brother Mikey took it down to the small inlet beside the slipway where the boats came in. We put it in the water and ran along the bank.

'See it, Mikey,' I shouted. 'See how it tacks into the wind like Father's boat.'

We raced the boat until it was too dark to see its sail.

Every Saturday, Grandfather took me across the bridge into Fisher's Lane market where the fish were sold. Here, he laid out his carvings on an old blue shawl my mother had given him. We stayed there until it grew dark and the market closed for another week. Then we went to the harbour to look at whatever ships were docked.

On one particular evening, there were a lot of trading ships from other countries. We listened to the sailors as we walked down the quayside. They

spoke in languages we did not understand.

'What was it like to be away at sea?' I asked.

Grandfather, a merchant sailor for many years, was full of stories of his adventures.

'It was hard, lad, but the great thing about it was we got to see the world.'

I held his hand as I skipped along beside him.

'And what's the best place you've ever been?'

He didn't have to think too long.

'That would have to be Tangiers.'

'On the north coast of Africa.' I knew all the place names by heart from listening to tales of his adventures. 'And what was it like?'

'Oh lad, it was beautiful. So hot we'd jump from the ship right into the sea to keep cool. Not a lot of the men could swim, but by the time we left the harbour, I could jump from the cross-sails.'

I had to run to keep up with his long strides.

'Where else?'

'Let's see now. Tarifa in Spain, across from Gibraltar.'

'And did you ever bring anything back from those places?'

'No, but I always tried to carve something to help me remember where I had been. In Egypt, it was a camel I saw one day near the harbour, and in Spain I remember carving a bullfighter. He was carried through the streets of the town because he had defeated the bull.'

'Where did all the carvings go?'

Grandfather shook his head.

'I lost them … over the years.'

We made our way home, talking about the places he had been. It was October. We sat around the fire, me and my brother Mikey, my mother, my baby sister Saoirse on my father's knee, and Grandfather on his bed. Father spoke as he cleaned out his pipe.

'The catch was poor again today. Let's hope it picks up soon.'

'What will you do?' my mother asked. There were a lot of mouths to feed in the house.

'We'll have to go further out to the fishing grounds west of the islands. That's bound to bring us a bit of luck.'

The next day was stormy and the boats stayed moored. I went down to the small beach near our house. My friend Annie was already there, watching the waves break on the shore. We played catch the waves for a while, dancing in and out at the very edge of the sea.

'Do you want to come to the Aran Islands tomorrow?' I asked. 'Father is planning a fishing trip if the weather gets better.'

Annie's face lit up. Her father was the shoe mender and they did not have a boat.

In the morning the sea was calm and I knew we would go. Grandfather decided to come along so we set off early in my father's boat. Mikey wanted to come too.

'No,' said my mother. 'Not this time.'

We sailed west until we saw Inis Mór, the big island, loom into view. My father tied the boat at the pier and Annie laid out a picnic on a rock. We had the tea my mother had put in a tin can, and some oatcakes with bread and cheese. Then my father set off again, promising to be back before sunset. The

three of us started the walk across to Dún Aengus, the ancient fort on the other side of the island. It was a steep climb and Grandfather grew tired.

'Leave me here and go off with you, but don't go near that cliff now. I'm warning ye.'

'We won't,' I shouted back.

We scrambled up the rest of the hill and saw the ancient fort of stone. There was a great view of the other islands. We stood for a while and then made our way down. I stopped at the entrance to the fort and looked at Annie.

'Let's see if we can spot a gull's nest.'

'We'd better be careful near the cliff,' she said.

'I know, I know. Come on.'

We headed towards the cliff edge. I peered down. The water was far below and there were no nests that I could see.

'Let's go back,' said Annie.

We were about to retrace our steps when, out of nowhere, a seagull flew in from the sea, swooping very low, right across our heads. I tripped and stumbled forward on the slippery grass. The swirling sea came towards me as I fell over the cliff. I landed hard on a flat piece of rock a few feet below the edge. My foot throbbed with white-hot pain and I closed my eyes, too scared to look.

Annie was calling to me but I could barely hear her above the screaming of gulls and the crashing waves below.

'Richard, quick, quick. Look up! Give me your hand.'

But I didn't want to open my eyes. I knelt, holding on to a small piece of rock that stuck out from the cliff face.

'I can't.'

My voice was only a whisper.

'Come on, Richard. Come on. It's not so far. See, my hand is just above you. I can pull you back up. Look!'

So I opened my eyes and there was Annie with her hand almost touching the top of my head. I reached up slowly, my fingers icy and shaking.

'That's it. That's it. Come on.'

We heard Grandfather shouting our names and at that moment I felt Annie's hand grab the tips of my fingers and then my wrist.

'Now, hold tight. I'm going to pull you up. Hold on.'

I thought my arm would break. The pain shot through me. I was too scared to look up but I listened to Annie's voice.

'I have you. We're almost there. Hold on. You're nearly up.'

I wanted to scream but my voice was gone. My legs were shaking. The wind hurt my ears. I searched for footholds in the cliff face with my knees and feet, scrabbling to get up. Annie held onto my wrist and, after what seemed like a long time, I gripped the top of the cliff and was able to pull myself up to the flat grass where Annie lay. Her arms were bleeding where she had scraped them on the rocks. I heard Grandfather calling us again. A few minutes later he came stumbling across the grass. He was out of breath.

'Are ye all right?' he asked. 'I got worried.'

I stood up but I was a little dizzy so I sat back again beside Annie. Grandfather took out his handkerchief and mopped her arms.

'What happened?'

'I fell,' I managed to whisper. 'Annie saved me.'

Grandfather shook his head as if he could not believe our luck.

'Well, lad you have yourself a brave friend here in Annie.'

'I know,' I said. 'Thanks Annie.'

She smiled. Her lips were blue and trembling.

'We'd better get back. Your father will be landing soon.'

We could hear him whistling before we saw the boat. He had had a good catch. We walked slowly towards the pier. By the time the boat pulled in, my arms and legs were beginning to feel better and I was no longer limping.

Grandfather said nothing about the fall and neither did Annie. She pulled her jumper over the scratches on her arms. We would never again go on a trip if my father knew what I had done. But it was all I could think about on the way home and all that night. Grandfather was right – Annie had been very brave.

We went back to playing on the beach every day and feeding the swans at the slipway. The winter set in and the weather worsened. The fishing catch got smaller and smaller. One day, as I came home from the beach, Grandfather called to me from his usual place.

'Come here lad, it's time I taught you a bit about carving.'

I sat on a low stool beside him and took the small knife and piece of bogwood he handed me. Then I watched his hands and copied what he did as best I could. I grew tired of holding the knife but all the same I stayed by his chair, my eyes fixed on his hands. The first thing he taught me to carve was a Galway hooker, which is a boat with two sails. It took me three afternoons and, when it was finished, Grandfather patted my head.

'Now go and show your mother,' he said.

The next Saturday, I went to the market as usual, only this time I put out the boat I had managed to carve on my own. After that I worked with Grandfather every day until we had enough carvings to sell on our Saturday trip.

As the cold days set in and the frost began to bite, Grandfather started to cough. It got worse, until there came a day when he did not take his stool to sit outside. After that, he spent most of his time in bed near the fire.

On Saturdays, I walked by myself to the market to sell the carvings. When it closed, I rambled down to the harbour to read the names of the ships from foreign lands, and listen to the voices using words I didn't understand. I longed to walk up the gangplank of one of those ships and take to the seas for my own life of adventure.

One morning, there was a lull in the bad weather which had kept the fishermen docked for weeks. In the grey silvery light of that dawn, I heard my father getting ready with the other men. They set off for the fishing grounds before the first rays of sun hit the water but they were gone only a few hours when thunder rolled in from the bay. The day darkened and the wind began to pick up.

For the rest of that day and long after darkness had fallen, the women and boys of the village stood on the shore with their lamps to guide the fishermen home.

The boats struggled ashore in ones and twos, the men soaked and exhausted. The Burkes, the Currans, Johnny 'The Mackerel' Kelly, our next door neighbour, the Jones' brothers, Mike Noone and his cousin Frankie 'The Cod'.

All the boats came in except the one my mother and I stood waiting for. The villagers stood with us through the long night and into the cold dawn. The thunder stopped and so did the rain. As I remember it now, it was a beautiful pink sky that broke over the flattened sea.

The long mourning cries of the women began and I knew my father wasn't coming home. My mother wrapped Saoirse under her shawl and walked up to our house, her head bowed and Mikey hidden in her long skirts. The lamps were put out. The men, who had come in earlier, silently took to the sea again to catch sight of any wreckage.

I stood alone on the slipway and looked across the bay. I had longed for the day when I would take my place beside my father in our boat. Then I would have him to myself during long fishing trips to learn the ways of the sea, the inlets to avoid, the tides and currents which were as familiar to him as the lines on his hands. I turned from the sea with tears stinging my freezing face. I knew at that moment my boyhood had ended. I was twelve years old. We had no boat, Grandfather was sick and there was nothing ahead but hungry times.

In the days that followed, the men of the village took to the sea, when the weather allowed, searching for my father's boat. All they ever brought home was one of the oars. After that they went back to fishing. The next Saturday, I crossed the bridge and headed towards the harbour. I walked the quays looking for work. Even though there were a lot of ships sheltering from the bad weather, none of them seemed to be looking for boys my age. As I was about to turn for home, I met a man I recognised from the fish market.

'You looking for work, lad?'

'Yes,' I said.

'Then try that tall ship there at the far end. They're heading for Spain with a full cargo but they might be looking for a cook's help. I heard one of them asking around a few days ago.'

An hour later, I had the job. The ship was leaving the following day and would return to Galway in the spring. I hurried home to tell Mother and Grandfather.

Tears streamed down my mother's face.

'Oh Richard, must you leave us now?'

But she knew there was no choice. Later that day I called to Annie's house. She wasn't surprised by my news. With the boat gone, there was no other way to make a living. As I was leaving, she called me back.

'Wait, Richard. I have something for you.'

She handed me a small knife. It had a shiny red handle. It was beautiful. We walked down to the slipway.

'Goodbye, Annie,' I said, my voice choking on the words.

She looked at me. Her face was pale and she did not smile.

'Take care of yourself, Richard. I'll pray always for your safe return.'

As she turned for home, I stayed watching the swans. I could hear Mikey shouting as he played at the back of our cottage. That evening we sat around the fire. Nothing much was said. Grandfather struggled against the constant cough he had since the winter began.

It was daybreak when I left. Everyone in our house was up. My mother gave me some bread and cheese wrapped in cloth, and kissed me. I hugged Saoirse and Mikey, and told Mikey to be good and not to fight with his sister.

He nodded and took my hand in his. We walked to the bridge.

'Go back, Mikey' I said. 'Home to Mam.'

Grandfather walked all the way to the harbour with me, although I could see it was hard for him. When we got to the ship, he put his arm around me.

'Richard lad, take care of yourself and come home to your mother. We'll all miss you.'

I nodded but I couldn't speak. As I walked up the gangway of the tall ship for the first time, men were hoisting sails and pulling in ropes. The boards of the old ship creaked and groaned and everyone seemed to be yelling orders at each other. A sailor patted me on the head and smiled. I could smell food cooking – spicy, exotic smells.

I stood watching Grandfather as the ship pulled away from the quay. In the grey light of the morning, we slid out into the bay. Everyone from the village had gathered on the beach to wave goodbye. I could see Mother holding Saoirse, and Mikey waving hard. Annie was there and the men who had tried to find my father's boat. Our tiny row of cottages got smaller. I was glad no one came near me as I fought to keep the tears back.

I stood on the deck for a long time watching as the bay disappeared and we headed for the open sea. Then I took my belongings below. The cook showed me where to sleep, on a narrow little bed high above two others. The room was dark and stuffy, and had many more bunks. I was beginning to feel sick. All I wanted was to lie down, but it was time to go to the kitchen – another dark and narrow room.

By now we were on the open sea and the ship lurched from side to side. I held on to a table to keep my balance. It was a Spanish ship so I had to

listen hard and try to learn fast. The cook, Pedro, was a small man with a big moustache. He wore a red handkerchief tied around his head and his skin was a deep walnut brown. He pointed to a pitcher of water.

'Agua.'

'Agua,' I repeated. He smiled, clapped me on the shoulder and laughed.

'Si! Bien. Muy bien.'

He walked to the other side of the kitchen.

'Carne,' he said, pointing to some meat hanging from a hook.

'Carne,' I said after him.

So it went on the first day. I learned the words quickly. The cook was a kind man and he always made sure to give me a plate of food before the sailors came for their meal. The men ate beside the galley on a wooden table, which Pedro showed me how to scrub. My other jobs were to wash dishes, keep the kitchen tidy, lay the table with mugs, forks and plates, peel onions and potatoes, and to take a tray to the captain. He ate alone in his cabin. His white beard was always trimmed and he wore a jacket with gold buttons. He was the only one of the crew who spoke English.

Every day when the sailors finished, I took the dishes to the galley and washed everything before putting them back on the shelf ready for the next meal. When I had done my work I was allowed to roam the ship, but at first I was so tired I just lay on my bunk. It wasn't the work so much as trying to follow what was said and repeating the words for different things.

Our first port of call was Bordeaux. We took on bags of flour and maize. After that we set sail again. Gradually, I got to know the sailors. The man in the bunk below me was called Sanchez. He played the banjo in the evenings

– beautiful music that seemed to fill the ship. The crew played cards and dice but I never learned the games. They spoke too fast and played for money so I usually just sat on deck. I found a small seat that was sheltered from the wind where I spent the nights carving until it grew too dark to see. I used pieces of turnip which I carved with Annie's knife. One evening as I sat there, I heard footsteps. It was the captain. He stood beside me and took the carving from my hands. It was a likeness of the ship. He turned it round and round.

'Muy bueno,' he smiled and nodded. 'Very good,' he repeated in English.

'Gracias. Thank you,' I said, and made a small bow.

He left and a little while later came back with a piece of bogwood from the cargo hold. I bowed.

'Gracias, señor.'

After that, the captain continued to give me pieces of wood and I returned carvings of the ship and one of himself, which he liked a lot. Then, of course, I had to do a likeness of Pedro and, after that, I was kept busy carving different figures the other sailors wanted. They gave me a nickname, 'Espadin,' which means 'little swordsman' in Spanish.

We were bound for Tarifa, where Grandfather had carved the little bullfighter. Now I would see it for myself and maybe bring back my own carving to him.

'You are the little mascot for our ship,' Captain said one evening, as he walked near where I sat. He looked down at me and smiled. 'You are our lucky mascot to save us from bad things.'

But I didn't. One morning, I heard shouts on deck. Everyone scrambled from their bunks. I couldn't understand what they were saying. The ship's lookout had climbed to the highest point – the bird's nest – and was shouting and pointing to a dark shape that was coming across the water from the east. Pirates! There was chaos. The captain shouted his orders. The cannon was made ready to fire. The men loaded guns with powder and drew their swords. But the ship sailed on towards us. Our cannon struck the bow but even so they were upon us within minutes. They fell upon our crew and a savage battle began. I had no sword and, even if I had, I wouldn't have known what to do. Everywhere I looked there were men fighting, their swords flashing against the sunlight. On the far side of the deck, Pedro lay groaning against the ropes. His sword had fallen. I crawled through the legs of the fighting men until I could reach it. I closed my hands on the handle. It was the first time I had held a sword in my hand. I looked up.

'Pedro!' I screamed.

I threw the sword towards him and he managed to grasp it. As soon as he had it in his hand, he let out a roar and threw himself into the fray. The smell of burning cannon and smoke filled the air. I crouched under the ropes, coughing and spluttering. But it was soon over. We had been taken by surprise and, within half an hour, the pirates had control of our ship. Many of our crew lay dead or dying on the deck.

They rounded up everyone who had survived and pushed us into the hold with the stocks of grain and flour. In the darkness, all I could hear were the moans of wounded men. I must have fallen asleep because the sound of the hatch creaking open jolted me. Through the white floury dust I saw Sanchez in a corner on the far side and near him lay Pedro, who was wounded. There was no sign of the captain but I knew they would have forced him to walk the plank. A man shouted something from above and handed in a barrel of water. We drank quickly, using our hands. The wounded men were given some too and after a few minutes, the hatch was closed again.

I don't know how long we were there. It may have been a few days. It may have been longer. When the hatch opened again we were told to get out. We struggled up the ladder into hot sunlight. Our captors stood on deck, about ten of them, all carrying swords. The ship was docking at a quay. My head swooned in the searing heat and I heard shouting. To my surprise, all of the men on the quayside had dark skin.

The gangway was lowered and three of the pirates pushed us forward, prodding with their swords. We shuffled on to dry land for the first time in many weeks. The red dust from the ground filled the air. My throat felt raw and my eyes burned. The men dragged us along the quay, shouting at us. We struggled down a long, narrow alley which opened onto a busy square. The place was swarming with people, selling everything from live birds to rolls of bright cloth. Our captors shoved us towards a large wooden cage. Sanchez stopped walking but was kicked immediately by one of the men. Some of the sailors tried to run but they had no chance. The door was shut and tied with wire. We had to crouch down. A crowd gathered. Some put their faces up close to us and pointed; others pulled our hair and laughed.

People wandered from stall to stall. They all wore long clothes, unlike any I had seen before. There were food stalls all about and we could smell meat cooking. It was so long since we had eaten or drank anything. No one in our group said much and, even when they did, I couldn't understand. My few words of Spanish seemed to have disappeared. The day wore on. I must have fainted because when I woke it was cooler and there were fewer crowds.

A large man came forward and opened the cage. He poked us through the bars and we climbed out. Then the haggling began as men looked us up and down and bargained with the pirates. I thought of the market where Grandfather and I would watch the fishmongers haggle over the price of their fish.

There was a lot of arguing and before we knew it we were sold. Our captors left, laughing among themselves. There were now four men in charge of us and they spent their time dancing around, pulling at our clothes and pushing us with sticks. We shuffled through the hot red sand. It made a good spectacle for the people and there was a lot of laughing and high pitched shouts from the women at the stalls. We went through a dark alley, which led into another street. People stood at shop doors to watch the procession. I felt a hand push me hard in the back and I fell forward. My face hit the ground and I tried to wipe the dust from my eyes. Some of the little wooden carvings fell from my shirt pocket. I tried to hide them quickly with my hand but someone knelt down in front of me, gathering them up. I covered my head waiting for a blow. But none came. I felt a hand on my elbow and I was helped to my feet.

The man who stood beside me was dressed in the same long clothes as everyone else except his were of a finer cloth. He held the carvings in his hand and I saw that he also had the knife Annie had given me. I looked down at the ground. He walked over to the man at the head of our group and spoke to him in a low voice. After a few minutes, I saw his hand reach into his clothes and pull out a little bag. Then I was taken by one of the slave traders and left standing beside the man who, it seemed, was my new owner.

There was no time to say goodbye. Sanchez, Pedro and the others were led away and I never saw any of them again.

I followed my new owner down narrow streets. This time there was no pushing or shouting. Sometimes he turned to make sure I was still behind him. But I didn't even think of running away. Where would I go? It was pitch black when we stopped at a large gate. A man, a servant I supposed, came and unlocked it. We entered a courtyard. My owner took me to a stone seat underneath a tree and disappeared into the black night. After a while, the same man who had opened the gate reappeared with a pitcher of water, and a plate of meat and rice. I drank quickly. He gestured me to eat. Never before or since has food tasted so good.

When I had finished, he led me across the courtyard to a small room with a bed and an oil lamp burning low. A set of fresh clothes lay on the bed – long, loose and white, like the people of this place wore. He showed me a basin of water and then left. I took off the raggy shirt and trousers I had worn since I left home, and washed. Then I put on the long robe and crept into the bed. Everything felt so good – the smell of clean clothes, the crisp sheets. I slept immediately. Later, I learned that I had slept for almost two days. When I did finally wake, I lay with the sheet over my head, not wanting the dream to end. For that is what I thought it was. If I opened my eyes, the bed and the quiet room would disappear. I would be in a shack somewhere with the others from the crew or in the dark hold of the ship with the smell of blood in my nostrils.

I heard someone at the door. The servant stood there, with a cup of the coldest, freshest orange juice and some fruits I did not know. I had been lucky. I was still a slave but to a good man. I thought of my father. Was he looking after me, wherever he was?

That evening I saw my new master again. He was a tall man, like Grandfather. He came into the courtyard with a girl who was about my age, maybe a little older, and drew a little ball from his robe. They began to toss it back and forth. The girl ran this way and that, shouting and laughing. I watched them from the doorway of the room, longing for those days when I had laughed and played like that with Annie and Mikey. It seemed like a very long time ago now. When the game was over, my new owner looked up and saw me. He crossed the courtyard and reached into the deep pockets of his robe. He brought out the carvings and my knife. He looked at them carefully, and then opened my hand and placed them there.

The next day the servant came to my room and gestured me to follow him. At the gates, my master was waiting. I followed him back through the long alleyways to the street where I had fallen. He stopped at one of the bigger shops and opened the door. I blinked as we entered the dark interior. Everywhere, set out on little shelves, were intricately carved pieces of silver and gold: beautiful jugs, goblets, rings, bracelets, necklaces and pendants. The room was large. A big table at one end was covered with unfinished carvings and tools. He pointed towards it.

I stood blinking in the shaft of sunlight from the door. I was to become his assistant; learn the craft. This was slavery of another sort. I would stay here in this room carving jewellery until I was an old man like Grandfather.

My master seemed to guess what I was thinking. He crossed the room and put his arm around my shoulder, towering above me. He pointed to himself.

'Abdul.'

And then he pointed to me.

'Richard,' I said.

He took up a tool to work on a small piece of silver. I sat beside him
and watched, in the same way I had watched Grandfather, sitting on a stool
outside our cottage. I would have to put that behind me, lock it away in a
corner of my heart and get used to my new life. That was how I spent my
first day, sitting with my master watching, learning. After that, I went every
day to Abdul's shop. I learned to clean the kiln where he fired metal. I began
to file and polish the pieces he was working on. My fingers became raw from
the hard edge of the file.

One morning as I was taking some metal from the kiln, a man entered the shop. When he saw me, he spoke in English.

'And who are you, young man?'

Apart from the ship's captain, these were the first words of English I had heard since I left home.

'My name is Richard Joyce.'

'And from where did you sail?'

'From Galway, on the west coast of Ireland, on a Spanish ship bound for Spain.'

I told the stranger about my adventure – how pirates took our ship and how we were sold as slaves. He listened and nodded. Then I asked him:

'Pray sir, what is the name of this place?'

'Algiers. This is the country of Algeria, and Abdul, your owner is a most renowned craftsman.'

Then the stranger spoke in French to Abdul. I recognised the tongue from hearing it spoken on the quays in Galway. Abdul nodded and looked at me.

'Irlande?'

I nodded.

Many people who spoke English visited the shop. I learned news of the world outside and was able to send a letter home but I gave no return address. I was still a slave, not a free man who could come and go as he pleased. I learnt to speak Arabic. Abdul taught me the names of every tool and every type of gem. In the evenings, we would walk back together as the sun set, to his home, a place I grew to love. He had four daughters who played together in the courtyard. Everyone came out at sundown for the heat during the day was very intense and people tended to stay in the coolness of

their houses. But the evenings were filled with the sound of children running back and forth, the men talking and the laughter of the women. Abdul had a large household of servants, and his wife Aisha had brought her mother and sister to live there too. The family gathered in the courtyard and shared a meal set out on a long table. I loved the food and the smell of spices that filled the air.

I taught the girls some English words and Zahra, the girl nearest to me in age, taught me how to play the flute. Soon I could play entire tunes. One evening, Abdul came to my room, carrying a beautiful carved flute.

'Take it, my friend. You have proved a hard worker and I know now that you will become a good smith.'

I bowed and took the gift.

'Thank you, sir.'

After that Zahra and I often played tunes together. The rest of the family listened and clapped.

The days seemed to blend together. I learned to carve rings, then bracelets. First, I practised using soft metals. Then I began to work in gold and silver, and learned how to grade the metals that came to our shop. Abdul taught me everything and I soaked up the knowledge like a sponge. It became my whole life. I rarely thought of home when I was at my bench in the shop. Only when I returned to my room, with its pinkish walls, and waited for the bell for dinner time, did my thoughts stray to my beloved Claddagh. Sometimes I thought of Grandfather. Was his cough better? Was Mikey a help to Mother? But, when the bell rang, I left those thoughts behind. Mostly, I tried to busy myself and shut it all away.

One day Abdul and I were sitting side by side at our benches. He raised his head.

'You have become a good goldsmith, Richard.'

'I still have much to learn.'

'So do we all, my friend. But that is why we sit here. Every day of my life I learn something new. You must always have open hands that are willing to learn from the metal itself. You must not subdue it. You must let it teach you – that way you are always learning.'

We continued to work in silence. Then he stopped and put down his work again.

'There is a great competition in Algiers among all the goldsmiths to make a piece of jewellery. The prize is a bag of gold,' he paused. 'I wondered whether you might think about it? Design something yourself?'

I shook my head.

'No, master. I could not do it.'

'It would be a good thing for you,' said Abdul. 'When I was a young man this is how I learned to be a smith. It is one thing to be able to carve, this takes skill, but it is another to design. This comes from your head, and your heart. You must start with a good idea and put all of yourself into making it with great passion.'

I said nothing but I thought about what he said and I knew in my heart he was right. I had become a skilled craftsman but I had not learned to create the magnificent rings and necklaces that brought people from all quarters to our shop. I agreed to enter. Abdul was pleased and gave me a beautiful piece of gold to work on but first I needed an idea. I tried to think of what to do but nothing came to me. I would make a ring, but what kind of ring? I looked at the plants and flowers in the garden. I looked at the birds that sang in the trees of the courtyard. But still no idea came to me. The next day I spoke to Abdul.

'I cannot enter the competition. I don't know enough. I have no ideas.'

He shook his head, smiling.

'Yes you have, Richard. Open your heart, look inside. Find what is there.'

That night, as I sat in my room, I thought about all the people I had known. Sometimes it was hard for me to remember their faces. I had spent so much time trying not to think of home that I had almost forgotten how they looked. But what I did remember were their hands. It seemed to me that I had spent my whole life watching people's hands – at Grandfather's knee watching his great hands carving pieces of bog oak, and my beloved father carefully mending his nets. What I remembered most about my mother was the way she rolled dough for bread on our kitchen table and how she stroked Saoirse's hair as we sat by the fire. So many hands – Annie pulling me up the cliff, Abdul picking me from the street, Zahra's fingers on the flute.

Every day, in between my other jobs, I worked on the ring. Abdul never asked to see it. I think he was just glad to see me working and content. Then one day as he closed the shutters on the shop, I called him over to the table. He picked up the ring I had made. For a long moment he stared at it and said nothing. When he spoke at last, his voice was low and serious.

'You have made a very beautiful ring, Richard, very beautiful indeed.'

Then we sat together and I explained. The heart at the centre of the ring signified the love I had for the people who were dear to me and the hands that held it were for the friendships I had known growing up in the Claddagh. The crown above the heart was for loyalty. These were all the things that meant the most to me.

For the first time, I spoke of home, my father and mother, Grandfather, Saoirse and Mikey. I told him about the night my father was lost at sea and how the people of the Claddagh had gone for days to search for him. I told him about Annie, how she saved my life that day on the cliff. Abdul listened to my story without speaking. He simply nodded from time to time but he never spoke or asked a question. It was late when we got back to the house and dinner had already begun.

Some weeks later Abdul came to my room. He opened my hand and gave me a bag. I stared at it.

'What is this?' I asked.

Abdul smiled at me.

'Take it, Richard. You have won the competition.'

When he left, I sat on my bed. I had never seen so many gold pieces. None of it made any sense. I was now wealthy and yet I was still a slave. The money was useless to me but I had won the competition with my ring.

More days passed, turning into weeks and months. I had little sense of how long I had been there. The seasons were all the same to me. I got used to the heat, the language, even the loneliness. Every day I went with Abdul to the shop and every day I learned something new from the metal in my hands and I was always surprised to hear my master pull the shutter closed. The years passed quickly.

One morning a stranger, dressed in European clothes, entered the shop. Abdul stood up from the table and went to greet the man, who spoke in English.

'I am looking for someone who works for you. His name is Richard Joyce.'

The air was very still and no one spoke. Then I rose slowly from the table.

'I am the one whom you seek.'

The stranger looked at me. He drew a piece of paper from his pocket and handed it to me.

'Do you know what this is?'

I shook my head.

'This is the King's order for all slaves taken in acts of piracy.' The man looked into my eyes. 'Richard Joyce, I am here on behalf of his Majesty, King William of England. You are now a free man.'

I stared at the paper. Something amazing had happened. I was free to go. It was hard to take it in. I looked up at the stranger.

'And this means?'

'You can go home, wherever that is.'

Home. Galway. The Claddagh. The words swam in my head, those place names I never thought I'd have any reason to say again. I could go home. I looked across and saw Abdul, his head bowed, standing at the other side of the table and I felt my heart break. What I had not wanted to see, now became clear.

The stranger left. My master leaned on the table.

'Let us return to our work'.

I sat down and picked up the bracelet I was working on.

Abdul did not refer to the visitor again and so neither did I. It was as if none of it had happened. But all I could think of was home. How old were Mikey and Saoirse? Was Grandfather still alive? How had my mother kept the family together? And Annie? I hardly dared to think of Annie. Had she married? Did she still live in the Claddagh?

It was the same the following day and the day after that. My master never spoke of the visitor. Sometimes I looked up to find him gazing at me with sadness. A few days later I was working on a new bracelet, which I had designed myself, when he came over to me. He picked up the ring that had won the competition. I always kept it close to me.

He examined the ring and, without looking at me, spoke the words I had been waiting for him to say.

'Richard, I do not want you to go. Stay. I will share my business with you. You will become a very wealthy man. My home is your home. Everyone here loves you. It is where you belong now.'

I put down my work.

'Abdul, you gave me a home. You taught me so much. But I must go back.'

He did not look at me nor I at him but we both knew that our days together in the shop had come to an end. That was the last time we walked home through the alleyways together. I told Zahra later that night. She held my hand and looked into my eyes.

'You are sure of what you are doing?'

I shook my head.

'No. I do not know what awaits me when I go back. It has been such a very long time.'

'But it is what you want?'

I nodded.

'Then go, Richard. My father will be all right. He still has the rest of us.'

For the first time, I realised that it had been hard for Zahra that her father made such a fuss of me.

The next day, I headed to the harbour. I found a ship bound for Southampton and booked my passage to sail two days from then. On the day of my departure, I said goodbye to everyone in the family. Zahra walked me to the gates and hugged me.

'Take care of yourself, Richard.'

'I will.'

There was no sign of Abdul. I had not seen him in two days. There was nothing for it but to take my belongings and go. At the harbour, I walked through the crowds and found my ship. As I climbed the gangplank, someone called out my name.

Abdul stood a little apart from the other groups gathered on the quayside. I went back down to him. He opened his hand and held out the ring.

'Take it. It's yours to keep. Do with it what you wish.'

Everything I wanted to say to him stuck in my throat. He put his hand on my shoulder.

'Go, son. Go with all the blessings of my heart. You have given me so much joy and happiness. Now your family needs you. Go home to them, Richard.'

I wept. I stood there among the sailors and the tears streamed down my face. I lifted my hand to my heart.

'Abdul, I will carry you here always. Always.'

We hugged for a long time. It was time to go. I walked up the gangplank and when I turned at the top, he was gone. Abdul disappeared from my life just as quietly as he had come into it.

We docked in Southampton on a fine morning in May. From there, I boarded a ship to Dublin and then a coach. It was an afternoon in early June when we pulled in to Galway. Slowly, I made my way down through the narrow streets and across the bridge and turned left towards the Claddagh. My heart beat quickly and I could hardly breath as I walked. Our house was still not in view when a boy passed me on the road. There was something familiar about him. I turned to look after him only to discover that he had also turned to look at me.

'Mikey?' I asked. 'Is it you?'

'Richard?'

He had grown into a tall lanky boy, probably the same age as I was when I left all those years ago. He ran towards me, letting out a loud whoop which brought people running from nearby houses. We were standing on the road jumping up and down, hugging and slapping each other, when I felt a small tug at my hand. A beautiful girl with a halo of auburn hair stood looking up at me. I shook my head.

'It cannot be. Is it Saoirse?'

She nodded. I bent down and gave her a gentle hug. I suppose she hardly remembered me but, all the same, she knew who I was. I had not been

forgotten. Then they came from the houses and the lanes of the Claddagh, the same friends and neighbours who had waved to me on the damp morning I set sail. I took the few steps further to our cottage. My mother was at the door, pulling off her old apron. She squeezed me so hard that I thought I would stop breathing. She had aged, the years of struggle etched in her face. I looked into her eyes.

'Grandfather?'

She shook her head.

'He's dead two summers now, Richard.'

Mother led me by the hand into our house, which seemed to have shrunk over the years.

'He left something for you.'

She pointed to the shelf above Grandfather's bed. The warm glow of the wooden carving seemed to light up the room. I blinked back tears. It was a replica of my Father's boat.

We sat and talked over tea until the light began to dim and Mother rose to light the candle. At last I had the courage to ask.

'And what of Annie? What news of her?'

My mother's face was hidden in the shadow cast by the candle.

'Well, lad, why don't you see for yourself? She'll be finishing up any time now down at the fish market.'

I left our house and crossed back over the bridge. I must have passed her on my way home. The market was closing. People turned to stare at me. I had bought new European style clothes in Southampton and, compared to everyone else, I was very finely dressed. Then I saw her. She was dragging the wooden planks across the market to where they were stored. She was taller. Her fair hair escaped in long ringlets from the scarf she wore. I picked up one of the planks.

'May I be of any assistance?'

She stopped. The setting sun was to my back. She put up her hand to shade her eyes. Then she rubbed them hard. I stepped forward.

'Annie, its me.'

She let the plank fall and it clattered loudly on the cobble stones.

'Richard?'

Her voice wavered.

I reached out for her hand and she ran into my arms. I don't think we spoke at all. We stood looking into each other's eyes until everyone had packed up and gone and there was no other sound but the gentle lap of the river against the quay wall. This was the moment I had longed for and feared the most. What if she hadn't felt the same?

We walked back across the bridge, talking until we were both nearly hoarse. I told her about Abdul and his shop, the ring and the competition. We sat on the little wall below my house, watching the white shapes of the swans in the water.

A week later, I stole into Annie's house one evening when I knew her father was out. She had just sat down by the fire. I sat opposite in her father's chair. I did not speak but instead I reached into the fire and got a lighted stick. I threw it at Annie's feet. It was the way of the Claddagh, the way to ask for her hand in marriage. She looked at the sparks on the wood. I watched her face in the soft glow of the flames. She was so beautiful. Then she reached down and took the stick in her hand and threw it back at my feet.

'Do you mean it, Annie?' I said, taking her in my arms. 'Will you be my wife?'

She smiled up at me.

'Oh yes.'

And then we walked down to our favourite place where we always fed the swans when we were little. I told Annie about my dream of setting up my own jewellery shop. She smiled at me.

'You should do it, Richard. Abdul would be proud and so would your father.'

On a sunny morning in July, the most beautiful morning of my life, we strolled to the strand and there we exchanged our vows under the watchful eyes of all of the villagers.

I put my ring on Annie's finger. She wore it, the Claddagh ring, on her left hand, with the heart turned inwards to show that she was wed, and that her heart was taken, which it truly was.

GALWAY TODAY

For information about Galway visit our website at:

www.galwayonline.com

Galway has changed a lot since Richard lived in the Claddagh in the late
17th century, but places illustrated in the book can still be seen.

Our website has up-to-date photographs of Galway as it is today,
and lots more besides.

Next time you're on the Net, drop in and have a look!

If you like, you can send an email message to:
tales@galwayonline.com
Maybe you'd like to tell us what you think of the book?

All the best from Galway.